Learning through Songs

Department of Music Education
College of Music
Temple University

TEMPLE UNIVERSITY
COLLEGE OF MUSIC
MUSIC EDUCATION AND THERAPY
T.U. 012-00
PHILA., PA

Learning through Songs

by Gail Levin and Herbert Levin

Barcelona PUBLISHERS

FIRST EDITION

ISBN 0-962080-01-0

2 4 6 8 9 7 5 3 1

Distributed throughout the world
by
Barcelona Publishers
4 Whitebrook Road
Gilsum, NH 03448
800-345-6665

Cover design by Frank McShane

PRINTED IN THE UNITED STATES OF AMERICA

Contents

Introduction

Learning Through Songs was developed for classroom teachers, music teachers, and music therapists. These songs will enable you to foster 23 specific educational skills and concepts through the medium of music. The approach, founded on the natural appeal music has for young children, uses simple songs to teach or reinforce these skills and concepts.

The search for unique, stimulating songs that provide experience and practice in various skill areas is a challenge for even the best of teachers. Thus, the songs presented here are designed to supplement and enhance the ongoing classroom curriculum. They are short with repetitive parts and offer numerous opportunities for enthusiastic class discussions. Most songs are co-responsive. The pleasant associations children have with music should make them enjoyable as well as purposeful. Furthermore, those children experiencing difficulty with certain skills or concepts may find the song activities less threatening and, as a result, may be eager to participate and able to learn.

Details of the skills and concepts have been written by Dr. Nancy Safer, Director of The Council for Exceptional Children, and are described in the Objectives section following the song activities. Specific skills and concepts developed in a particular song are highlighted and further defined in the activity description for each song. Use this information in selecting song activities related to particular educational objectives for your class as a whole and for individual children.

These song activities and their applications were developed and tested by the authors, in consultation with Dr. Safer, based on over twenty years of experience in the Philadelphia Public Schools, working directly with children of all ages, ability levels and needs. This publication is a second editon of the original *Learning Through Songs,* published in 1977 by Teaching Resources (A New York Times Company) of Boston.

Before You Begin

This book contains 16 songs with suggestions for many variations. The songs are *not* presented according to level of difficulty. Each song activity is presented on two or more consecutive pages containing the music manuscript and the activity description. On each music manuscript page, parts of a song are labeled to indicate who is to sing each specific part.

Activity Description Page

Children Required

All the songs require the entire class. Most of the songs have solos; a few do not. The number given here specifies how many soloists are needed to perform the song in its original form. Variations of the song may require more or fewer soloists.

Lyrics

The format of the song and its words can be clearly seen by glancing at the lyrics. These will help you in selecting the song and the soloists. As on the music manuscript page, parts of the song are labeled next to the lyrics to indicate who is to sing each section. A dash (—) indicates a sustained note.

Specific Skills and Concepts Developed

Major skills and concepts developed in the song are listed and described here to aid you in finding the appropriate song activity for your children's needs.

Procedure

This section of the activity description suggests an order of procedure for introducing and teaching the song to your class. Use it as a guide, with your own modifications, to elicit the words of the song from the children as naturally as possible. Approaching the song activity in this manner should make extensive rote teaching of the words unnecessary.

Variations

Substituting different words in the song transforms one activity into many. Most variations foster additional skills and concepts not involved in the song activity in its basic form. Few variations are easier than the original song; most are more difficult. Unless otherwise suggested, it is best to do the song activity in its basic form before using the variations.

General Teaching Suggestions

Whether you are a classroom teacher who will be using a music program for the first time, or a music teacher or music therapist who will be working with learning-disabled children for the first time, the primary goal of the activities is to create therapeutic and enjoyable learning experiences for children through songs. The teaching suggestions offered here are intended to help you achieve this goal.

Although excellence in performance contributes to a child's sense of pride and accomplishment, attaining perfection will not always be realistic for your class. Learning takes place most effectively when activities are appropriate and motivating. Too much attention to words, pitch, or tone can rob the music sessions of their vitality, spontaneity, and essential aura of fun. Thus, when you introduce a song, do not press for exactness while the children are learning the words. Let preliminary class discussions and repeated use of lines from the song teach the words.

Inevitably, the responsibility for keeping the music-learning sessions interesting and alive falls on you. Good pacing is essential in creating successful learning experiences. Here are a few suggestions that should help you maintain proper pacing with the song activities:

- Alternate the performing children by giving each child several opportunities to participate in each music session.

- Alternate songs sung by the entire class only with songs using both the class and soloists.

- Alternate moods by following a poignant song with a lively one.

- Maintain an interchange with the children between activities by commenting positively about a child's appearance, feelings, or behavior and by discussing the concepts developed in a song.

Sometimes, children selected for solo parts — or even the entire class — may seem unaware of the musical accompaniment and rush through the responses at a very rapid pace, totally out of tempo. When this happens, stop the recorder. Explain the problem to the children and have them listen, without singing, to that part of the accompaniment. Hand movements made by you in time to the music also may help them "tune into" the tempo of a song.

You may find, occasionally, that children selected as soloists "talk" their responses rather than "sing" them. Some children may do this simply because they are self-conscious about singing before the class, and need support and encouragement. Other children may not be aware that talking differs from singing. Using your own voice to demonstrate lyrics "talked" versus lyrics "sung" may help these children grasp the difference and prompt them to experiment with their own voices.

Although the skills and concepts presented here are through the auditory medium of music, you may find instances when visual aids are useful in teaching a particular concept. For example, in the song that deals with contractions, a diagram on the chalkboard may make the process of combining two words more explicit to the children.

Many of the songs use question and answer format. At times, the response a child gives in a particular song may seem bizarre or simply erroneous. Before dismissing such an answer, however, it is important that you ask the child to explain or justify the response. For example, a child who responds "Yes" to "Can you touch the moon?" may justify that answer by explaining that if you have a rocket, you can go to the moon and touch it. Such responses demonstrate a high level of conceptualization and should be accepted.

Some children (especially young children) may feel self-conscious about singing a solo before a group. Your support, communicated verbally or through body contact (an arm around the shoulder, or a hug) may give them the reassurance and comfort they need to perform the task with success.

Remember these songs were designed to supplement the ongoing classroom curriculum. You are one of the key components, for much in the music-learning sessions will be an extension of yourself and your particular style of teaching. Only you can select the songs that suit the special needs of your particular class. Your vitality and enthusiasm will excite and motivate the children. Your use of facial expressions and body movements will convey to the class your feelings about the songs, the children, and their performance of the songs. Be the teacher that you are. Your commitment to the children and your intimate awareness of their personalities, abilities, and needs will make the program a successful learning experience for all.

Directing Techniques

- Giving precise and clear cues is essential to good directing. This kind of support will help children respond at the correct time and will reduce possible apprehension on their part. Use the directing techniques suggested here only as long as you feel they are needed. As soon as the children can sing their responses without cues from you, let them do so. Not directing the children honors their independence and contributes to their sense of achievement.

- Direct at the children's eye level in order to maintain eye contact with them.

- Position yourself as close to the class as possible. Proximity to the children will help keep them involved in the song and reduce possible fragmentation.

- Point or nod to each child and to the class when they are to sing their respective parts. Use your entire hand (as in a traffic policeman's signal) to stop a response or to keep as response from being sung at the wrong time. Don't hesitate to use exaggerated hand and body movements.

- For those songs with solos, rehearse or "dry run" each child's part before you begin. Successful practice experiences will give the children greater confidence and security.

Song #1: Rhyme Time

Lyrics		Children Required
All	It's rhyme time.	entire class
	It's rhyme time.	4 soloists
	Time to play a rhyming game.	
	Find some words that sound the same.	
1st solo	"**Play**" is a rhyme for "**day**."	
All	That's one rhyme.	
2nd solo	"Say" is a rhyme for "day."	
All	That's two rhymes.	
3rd solo	"**Stay**" is a rhyme for "**day**."	
All	That's three rhymes.	
4th solo	"**Way**" is a rhyme for "day."	
All	That's four!	
	It's rhyme time.	
	It's rhyme time.	
	Now we've played a rhyming game,	
	found some words that sound — the — same.	

Specific Skills and Concepts Developed

Cognitive: Language — *vocabulary building, sentence building, rhyming*

"Rhyme Time" is designed to help children explore sets of rhyming words. The lyrics of the song support the concept of *rhyming* by stressing the distinctive feature of words that rhyme — they sound the same.

Vocabulary building is fostered by new and different sets of rhyming words the children come up with. According to the ability level of the class, vocabulary building may be extended by forming two-syllable rhyming words. (See Variation.)

Sentence building is reinforced throughout the song by the use and repetition of complete sentences.

Procedure

• Suggest to the class a specific word like "cat." Then tell the children, "Think of some words that sound the same." Each child should have a turn naming a word that rhymes with "cat." In order to avoid duplicate answers and to also help some children think in terms of rhymes, it can be fun to find words by going through the alphabet. Limit this to words that begin with consonants and, with more proficient children, consonant blends.

• After the class has grasped the idea of rhyming, play and sing the song.

• Play the song again. This time have the class count the rhymes as they are sung. For example, "That's one rhyme." The children will notice there are four rhymes for "day."

• Play the song once again and have the class join in singing the four rhyming words, "play," "say," "stay," and "way."

• Now choose four children for the solo parts. Have each child sing one of the words above that rhymes with "day." Encourage the children to freely substitute additional sets of rhyming words for the solo responses once they become familiar with the song's musical form and words.

Variation

1. Discuss and sing two-syllable words that rhyme. For example: copy, sloppy, poppy, floppy, choppy.

Song #1: Rhyme Time

"Say" is a rhyme for "day." That's two rhymes. "Stay" is a rhyme for "day." That's three rhymes. "Way" is a rhyme for "day." That's four! It's rhyme time. It's rhyme time. Now we've played a rhym-ing game, found some words that sound the same.

Song #2: What's in Your House?

Lyrics

All What do you have in your house, in your house?

1st solo I have a **chair**

2nd solo I have a **bed.**

3rd solo I have a **lamp.**

4th solo I have a **stove.**

All Oh, they have a **chair, a bed, a lamp, a stove.**

Yes, in their houses.

Childen Required

entire class

4 soloists

Specific Skills and Concepts Developed

Cognitive: Classification — *general* and *restricted categories*

Language — *sentence building, pronouns, verbs, plurals*

"What's in Your House?" presents a *general category* of classification to children by asking them to name objects that may be found in a house.

More *restricted categories* requiring that the objects be named in *plurals* or be found in a particular place (a bedroom or a drugstore, for example) are presented in Variations, as are the most difficult classification tasks dealing with objects made of a specific material such as wood, metal, glass, and so forth. Whether you introduce these last classifications to your class will depend, of course, on the ability level of the children.

Sentence building, pronouns, and *plural verb* forms are reinforced throughout the song by their use and repetition.

Procedure

• Ask the class, "What do you have in your house?" As each child answers, encourage him or her to respond with a complete four-word sentence rather than with only a noun. These sentences form the nucleus of the lyrics for the song.

• Play and sing the song for the children.

• Once the class is familiar with the song's musical form and words, encourage the children to freely substitute additional objects found in a house for the solo responses.

Note: During the final two lines of the song, if you find the class is having difficulty remembering the objects that were sung about, point to each soloist as you sing the item he or she named.

Variations

1. Discuss and sing about the contents of any **one** room of the house (kitchen, bathroom, bedroom, living room, and so forth).

2. Select one child to sing the four solo parts. He or she may choose from one or many rooms in the house. Substitute either the child's name or "he/she" for "they." Sing, "his/her house" in the last line. Change the verb "have" to "has."

3. Discuss and sing about things found in your classroom (book, chalkboard, paper, pencil, door, desk, clock, and so forth). Sing, "What do we have in our room . . .?" The soloists respond by singing, "We have a book (chalkboard, paper)."

4. After singing about single items, ask the children to name items they have more than one of (plurals). For example:

> "I have two televisions."
> "I have three lamps."
> "I have six chairs."
> "I have ten spoons."

5. Discuss and sing about things found in drugstores and food stores, etc. Sing, "What do they have in drug (food) stores . . .?" The soloists sing, "They have toothpaste (catsup)," and so forth.

6. For Variations #1, #3, and #5, discuss and sing about items that begin with specific speech sounds. For example:

Variation #1	kitchen: *t*able, *t*easpoon
Variation #3	classroom: *d*oor, *d*esk
Variation #5	drugstore: *p*ills, *p*erfume
	food store: *b*ologna, *b*read

7. Name and sing about items made of: wood, glass, china, metal, plastic, paper, and so forth.

9

Song #2: What's in Your House?

Song #3: How Old Are You?

	Lyrics	**Children**
All	How old are you?	entire class
	How old are you?	1 soloist
	How old are you, my friend?	
Solo	I'm **nine years** old.	
	I'm **nine** years old.	
All	Gee, it's great to be **nine** years old.	
	Gee, it's great to be **nine** years old — .	
	Gee!	

Specific Skills and Concepts Developed

Cognitive: General knowledge — *age*
Language — *sentence building, pronouns, plurals, contractions*
Affective: Self-concept — *identity*

"How Old Are You?" requires the child to learn his or her correct *age*. Knowing his or her age expands the child's *identity*. The activities in Variations foster the awareness of age as a characteristic of all people and extend the concept of age from a personal to a general level.

Sentence building, pronouns, plurals, and *contractions* are explored and developed as the children sing first the original song and then its variations.

Procedure

• Ask a child in the class, "How old are you?" He or she will probably answer with just one word ("nine," for instance). Now ask the child again, saying, "This time make a four-word sentence."

• If the child answers, "I am nine years old," have the child count the number of words on his or her fingers while saying them. Point out that five fingers (words) were used. Then ask, "How can you shorten the sentence to just four words?" Many children will try a variety of ways. For example, they may say two words for one finger or drop the last word to avoid using the contraction for "I am." If there is too much delay, ask, "How can you make one word out of 'I am'?"

• Some young or handicapped children may count their ages on their fingers. In this case, do not have the children use their fingers for counting the four-word sentence. Simply rote teach the contraction.

• Play and sing the song for the children.

11

Note: Whenever the word "Gee" is sung, suggest that the children make fists and punch the air. Doing so not only is fun, but also accents the word as the children sing it. With a little encouragement, repetition of the word with the action can motivate even a shy child to join in.

Emphasize to the children the need to listen very carefully to the music at the end of the song. They must get ready for the last surprise "Gee!"

Variations

1. Choose several (about four) children of the same age to sing the solo part together. Have the class add an "s" to "friend." The four singers must now sing, "We're _____ years old."

2. Have a child sing about his or her brother or sister. Substitute the name of the brother or sister for "you." Use "He's/She's" in place of "I'm."

Song #3: How Old Are You?

Song #4: Now and Before

Lyrics

All	Let's take a word that tells about now and change it to tell about before
1st solo	If it's now, I **play.** "**I play**" tells about now.
All	Let's change it to tell about before.
1st solo	**I played!**
2nd solo	If it's now, **I dance.** "**I dance**" tells about now.
All	Let's change it to tell about before.
2nd solo	**I danced!**
All	"**I play**" was changed to tell about before.
(spoken)	**I played!** "**I dance**" was changed to tell about before.
(spoken)	**I danced!** We changed them from now to before.

Children Required
entire class
2 soloists

Specific Skills and Concepts Developed

Cognitive: Language — sentence building, past tense of verbs

"Now and Before" exposes children to systematic practice in distinguishing present tense and *past tense verbs.* The song focuses the children's attention on the exact nature of the change in tense they are making by introducing verbs that tell about now and then changing the same verbs to tell about before.

Sentence building is reinforced throughout the song by the use and repetition of complete sentences.

Procedure

• Discuss with the class *action* words, "words that describe things we do." Have the children name and demonstrate some action words such as "walk," "jump," "hop," "skip," "play," and "dance."

• Next, discuss the fact that different forms of a word are used to tell about *present* action and *past* action. For action that is happening *now,* we use "I walk." For action that happened *before,* we add "ed" to make "I walked."

• Tell the class, "We are going to sing a song about now and before." Introduce the song by having the children repeat the line, "Let's take a word that tells about now and change it to tell about before."

• Use the word "play." Ask the children, "If it's now, what would you say?" Response: "I play." Have the class repeat the lines, "If it's now, I play. 'I play' tells about now."

• Then ask the class, "How would you change 'I play' to tell about before?" Response: "I played." Have the children repeat the lines, "Let's change it to tell about before. I played!"

- Now use the word "dance." Follow the same teaching procedure.
- Play and sing the song for the class.
- Play it again. This time, sing the two solo parts and have the class sing as many of the lyrics as possible in the sections marked *All*.
- Choose two soloists to sing the solo parts.
- Once the class is familiar with the song's musical form and words, encourage the children to freely substitute additional verbs for the solo responses.

Note: On the music manuscript page in the last section marked *All*, the words "**I played**" and "**I danced**" are underlined. This is to draw your attention to the fact that they are to be spoken, not sung.

Initiate this activity with regular verbs only. Continue to use them until you are confident that the children observe the addition of "ed" to form the past tense.

Variation

1. Once the children have mastered the past tense of regular verbs, move on to the past tense of irregular verbs. For example:

> sing — sang
> think — thought
> run — ran
> fight — fought
> swim — swam

Initially, many children may try to apply the past tense rule for regular verbs to irregular verbs, producing words like "singed" or "thinked." With practice, however, the children will be able to differentiate between regular and irregular verbs.

Song #4: Now and Before

Very slowly (♩= 48 M.M.)

Words by **Nancy Safer**

(All)
Let's take a word that tells a - bout now and change it to tell a - bout be - fore. If it's now, I **play.** "I play" tells a - bout now. Let's change it____ to tell a - bout____ be - fore. I **played!** If it's now, I **dance.** "I **dance**" tells a - bout now. Let's

(1st solo)
(All)
(1st solo)
(2nd solo)
(All)

TEMPLE UNIVERSITY
COLLEGE OF MUSIC
MUSIC EDUCATION AND THERAPY
T.U. 012-00
PHILA., PA

Song #5: Everybody Makes Mistakes

Lyrics

All Everybody, Everybody makes mistakes*
sometimes,* sometimes.
Everybody, Everybody makes mistakes.
Everybody, Everybody makes mistakes*
sometimes,* sometimes.
Everybody makes mistakes.

Children Required

entire class

Specific Skills and Concepts Developed

Cognitive: Language — *vocabulary building*
Affective: Self-concept and Social Perception — *mistakes*

"Everybody Makes Mistakes" helps children put *mistakes* in perspective. Frequently, children view themselves as being inferior or bad for making mistakes. The song emphasizes that everybody makes mistakes sometimes and that mistakes are therefore universal experiences rather than personal experiences resulting from inherent deficiencies or "badness" in the individual.

The word "mistake" may be unfamiliar to some children. Vocabulary building is fostered by providing those children with a new label for a concept that is undoubtedly already a part of their experience — doing something wrong unintentionally.

Procedure

• It is effective to introduce this song to the class by making a predetermined "mistake" yourself. For example: spell a word incorrectly on the chalkboard, or drop a book on the floor. Express surprise at your action by saying, "Oh, I made a mistake!" Doing so will set a receptive mood for teaching the song.

• Discuss common types of mistakes the children will understand, such as accidents (spilling a drink), forgetfulness (leaving your boots at school when you go home), and thoughtlessness (doing or saying something that you are sorry about later).

• Throughout all of the discussions, include the statement, "Everybody makes mistakes." Then ask, "When?" The class will most likely answer, "Sometimes." These quotes make up the lyrics of the song. The children will learn the words very quickly if they are introduced in this manner.

• Play and sing the song to the class. Notice that the question "When?" is enthusiastically called out just before the word "sometimes." This is indicated on the music manuscript page and in the lyrics above by an asterisk (*).

Note: The musical phrases for "sometimes" are fun to sing in a sliding manner (a musical slur or legato).
After the words "makes" and "mistakes" there is a pause.
At the end of the song, after the word "makes," a complete stop is very effective.

Song #5: Everybody Makes Mistakes

Song #6: What Do You Say?

Lyrics

All   What do you say when you don't have time,
don't have time to say,
Teacher   "I am?"
All   We say "I'm."
"I'm" is what we say for "I am."
Oh, what do you say when you don't have time,
don't have time to say,
Teacher   "We are?"
All   We say "we're."
"We're" is what we say for "we are."
Oh, that's what you say when you put two
words together.
That's what you say when you don't — have —
time.

Children Required

entire class
1 soloist (Teacher)

Specific Skills and Concepts Developed

Cognitive: Language — *sentence building, contractions*

"What Do You Say?" is designed to allow you to select and present a variety of contractions to the class. The lyrics of the song emphasize that a contraction is simply an abbreviated form of a two-word phrase.

Sentence building is reinforced throughout the song by the use and repetition of complete sentences.

Procedure

• Begin to teach this song by saying to the class, "Let's think about the two words 'I am.'" Show one finger at a time for each word. Then ask, "How can they be changed into only one word?" ("I'm") For an additional hint, you might ask, "How would you shorten the two words?" If the class has not yet been taught contractions, you may have to resort to writing the two forms on the chalkboard. Then have the children compare them.

• Discuss the words "we are" in the same manner as above. Once the children grasp the idea, you can reinforce the concept and teach some of the words of the song by stating, "That's what you say when you put two words together."

• As soon as the concept has been strengthened, offer the children the opportunity to form many contractions.

• Play and sing the song to the class. At first use the contractions presented in the original lyrics. Once you and the children are familiar with the song's musical form and words, freely substitute additional two-word phrases they can make into contractions.

Song #6: What Do You Say?

don't have time, don't have time to say, "we are"? We say "we're." "We're" is what we say for "we are." Oh, that's what you say when you put two words to-geth-er. That's what you say when you don't have time.

Song #7: Yes, I Can

	Lyrics	**Children Required**
Solo	Oh, I can **clap my hands.** Yes, I can	entire class
All	Yes, (he/she) can.	1 soloist
(solo claps)		
Solo	Oh, I can **clap my hands.** Yes, I can.	
All	Yes, (he/she) can.	
(solo claps)		
Solo	Oh, I can **clap my hands.** Yes, I can.	
All	Yes, (he/she) can.	
(solo claps))		
Solo	Oh, I can **clap my hands.** Yes, I can.	
All	Yes, (he/she) can.	
(solo claps)		
Solo	Yes, I can	
All	Yes, (he/she) can.	
(solo claps)		
Solo	Yes, I can.	
All	Yes, (he/she) can.	
(solo clap)		
Solo	Oh, I can **clap my hands.** Yes, I can.	
All	Yes, (he/she) can.	
(solo claps)		
Solo	Yes, I can.	
All	Yes, (he/she) can.	
(solo claps)		
Solo	Yes, I can.	
All	Yes, (he/she) can.	
(solo claps)		
Solo	Oh, I can **clap my hands.** Yes, I can.	
All shout	Yes, (he/she) can !	
(solo claps)		

Specific Skills and Concepts Developed

Cognitive: Language — *sentence building, pronouns*
Affective: Self-concept — *positive self-concept*

"Yes, I Can" provides a flexible format through which a child's abilities can be emphasized. Skillful use of the song may help change the child's view of himself or herself from a negative self-concept (one who can't do very much) to a *positive self-concept* (one who can do a variety of things such as run, jump, sing).

Sentence building and *pronouns* are reinforced throughout the song by their use and repetition.

Procedure

• Choose a child or ask for a volunteer to stand with you in front of the class. Play and sing the song to the class. Encourage the child to sing the solo parts and the class to sing their parts with you. Cue each at the proper time. Have the soloist repeat the words, "Oh, I can clap my hands. Yes, I can." The soloist claps when the class sings, "Yes, she can."

• Once the class is familiar with the song's musical form and words, freely substitute other actions, ("ride a bike, bake a cake").

Note: You may wish to begin this activity by having the entire class sing, "Oh, we can clap our hands. Yes, we can."

Variations

1. Divide the class in half. One half sings and performs the selected action, "Oh, we can stamp our feet" (". . . snap our fingers," ". . . slap our knees," and so forth). The other half sings, "Yes, they can."

2. Have the soloist use one of the following instruments, if available, and change the words of the song accordingly:

> rhythm sticks
> wood block
> small drum
> resonator bell (B flat)
> tambourine
> triangle

Song #7: Yes, I Can

25

Song #8: Windy Wind

Lyrics

All I know the sunshine lights up the day.
I know the moonlight lights up the night.
But everybody knows,
everybody knows,
the windy wind — blows. Whooo____.
The windy wind — blows. Whooo____.

Children Required

entire class

Specific Skills and Concepts Developed

Cognitive: General Knowledge — *weather*
Language — *vocabulary building, sentence building*

"Windy Wind" introduces the concept of *weather* by presenting properties of the wind (it blows, making a distinct sound) and, in its Variation, properties of the snow (it falls quietly). The verses can trigger imaginative class discussions about wind and snow.

Vocabulary building is fostered in the song by words that describe the properties of wind and snow.

Sentence building is reinforced through the use of complete sentences.

Procedure

• Discuss with the class the concepts that sunshine lights up the day, moonlight lights up the night, and the wind blows. Introduce the concepts by asking, "What lights up the day?"; "What lights up the night?"; "What does the wind do?"; and "How does it sound when it is windy?" The sound for the wind in this song is "Whooo." When the children answer the above questions, encourage them to form complete sentences. For example, "The sunshine lights up the day." Have the class repeat the sentences. These form the nucleus of the lyrics for the song.

• Play and sing the song to the class.

• Before having them sing the entire song, first have them sing "Whoo" at the end.

Note: The musical phrases for "everybody knows" are fun to sing in a sliding manner (a musical slur or legato).

You may need to restrain the children from singing "blows" until the appropriate time. After "blows," they imitate the sound of the wind.

Variation

1. Substitute the words "quiet snow" for "windy wind," and "snows" for "blows." "Shhh" is the sound of the quiet snow.

Song #8: Windy Wind

Song #9: The Hungry Song

	Lyrics	Children Required
All	When you're hungry, what do you eat When you 're hungry, what do you eat ?	entire class 4 soloists
1st solo	I eat **fish.**	
2nd solo	I eat **beans.**	
3rd solo	I eat **steak.**	
4th solo	I eat **ice cream.**	
All	Then I'm not hungry anymore. Then I'm not hungry anymore.	

Specific Skills and Concepts Developed

Cognitive: Classification — *general* and *restricted categories*
Language — *vocabulary building, sentence building, pronouns, plurals*

"The Hungry Song" presents a *general category* of classification to children by asking them to name foods they like to eat when they are hungry. *Restricted categories* are explored in Variations that request specific types of foods. For example: meats, vegetables, desserts; foods eaten at breakfast, lunch, and so on.

Variations also present properties such as color, hardness, and taste and ask the children to classify and name foods characterized by these attributes. Whether you introduce these properties to your class will depend, of course, on the ability level of the children.

Vocabulary building is encouraged through the use of new and different words you or the children may suggest.

Sentence building, pronouns, and *plurals* are reinforced as the children sing first the original song and then its variations.

Procedure

• Ask the class, "When you're hungry, what do you eat?" Encourage each child to answer with a complete three-word sentence rather than with only a noun. These sentences form the nucleus of the lyrics for the song.

• When the children have completed naming their specific foods, discuss the fact that after you have eaten all you want, you say, "Then I'm not hungry anymore." Repeat the words of this section of the song that the entire class will sing later.

• Play and sing the song to the class.

• Once the class is familiar with the song's musical form and words, encourage the children to freely substitute additional foods for the solo responses.

Variations

1. Limit the four solo responses to one specific food category only. For example: meats, vegetables, fish, or desserts.

2. Limit the four solo responses to breakfast, lunch, or dinner foods only.

3. Use the song as a "Thirsty Song," naming things to drink.

4. Discuss and sing about foods with a distinctive property:

    hard — candy canes, nuts, apples, peanut brittle

    soft — peas, mashed potatoes, bananas, marshmallows, pudding

    colored — red: apples, cherries, beets, strawberries, orange: carrots, tangerines, oranges,
           green: spinach, peas, grapes, string beans, yellow: lemons, grapefruit, bananas

    sweet — cakes, candy, sugar, ice cream, cookies

5. Discuss foods eaten by animals. For example: cows eat grass; horses eat hay; elephants eat peanuts; mice eat cheese. Young children may enjoy acting out animal parts as they sing their solos.

6. Discuss and sing about foods and beverages that begin with specific speech sounds.

    For example:

        foods — *p*eas, *p*otatoes

        beverages — *c*ocoa, *c*offee

Song #9: The Hungry Song

31

Song #10: Learn About Things

Lyrics		Children Required
All	There are five ways, five ways to learn about things, learn about things: touch, taste, see, smell, hear.	entire class 1 soloist (Teacher)
Teacher	Can you **touch a tree?**	
All	Yes, we can. Yes, we can.	
Teacher	Can you **hear a song?**	
All	Yes, we can. Yes, we can. That's how we learn about things, learn about things, learn about many things.	

Specific Skills and Concepts Developed

Cognitive: General Knowledge — the five senses
Language — vocabulary building

"Learn About Things" provides children with labels for *the five senses.* Labeling the senses and then associating them with appropriate parts of the body introduces the concept of specific functions for various body parts.

In addition to learning labels for the senses, *vocabulary building is* fostered by introducing a variety of things the children must determine they can or cannot touch, taste, see, smell, or hear.

Procedure

• Tell the class, "There are five ways to learn about things." Have the children repeat the words in the first section of the song marked *All.* As the children say the word "five," tell them each to hold up five fingers. Now ask, "What are the five parts of your body that help you to learn?" To help the children make the associations, you might point out that two ways to learn begin with the letter "t," another two with the letter "s," and yet another with the letter "h." Then, as each sense is named, ask the children to name and point to the part of the body related to it.

• Introduce the lyrics of the song by asking the class some questions. "Can you touch the ground?" Response: "Yes, we can. Yes, we can." Or, "Can you touch the sky?" Response: "No, we can't. No, we can't."

• Play and sing the song to the class.

• Once the children are familiar with song's musical from and words, freely substitute additional sense/object pairs for the solo response questions.

Note: The first few times the class performs this song, it is a good idea for you to sing the solo questions. Later, depending on the ability level of the class, you may want to substitute a child to ask the solo questions.

If the children have a problem processing sentences, here is a progressive list of ways to present the solo questions:

1. Choose the same sense for both solos with questions requiring "yes" answers only.

2. Choose the same sense for both solos with one question requiring a "yes" and the other a "no" answer.

3. Choose two different senses for both solos with questions requiring "yes" answers only.

4. Choose any of the five senses for both solos with questions requiring "yes" and "no" answers.

Song #10: Learn About Things

34

Song #11: Some People

Lyrics

All 1. Some people can't **run** as fast as others
Some people can't **walk** as fast as others.
Some people can't **learn** as fast as others.
But all people, all people,
all people can be fast — at being — friends.

All 2. Some people can't **see** as well as others.
Some people can't **hear** as well as others.
Some people can't **talk** as well as others.
But all people, all people,
all people can be fast — at being — friends.

Children Required

entire class

Specific Skills and Concepts Developed

Affective: Social Perception — *friends, individual differences*
Cognitive: Language — *vocabulary building*

"Some People" introduces the concept that although some individuals may lack particular skills or abilities (the ability to see, hear, and learn rapidly, for instance), such people can still make good *friends*. The song is particularly effective and useful as a core for honest, open discussions about *individual differences* and/or handicaps.

Vocabulary building is explored as the children sing the words of the original song and is then expanded as they suggest new words for additional verses.

Procedure

• Discuss with the class the fact that some people can't run as fast as others. Ask the children to think of other ways in which people are different. End this part of the discussion with the specific words of the song ("run," "walk," "learn"). Have the class repeat the first three lines of the song. These sentences are part of the lyrics for the first verse.

• Now discuss what people have in common. Lead the discussion to the fact that all people can be fast at being friends.

• The song affords an excellent opportunity for you and the class to have a positive discussion about people with learning problems or with sight, hearing, speech, and other physical disabilities. Discuss how one should behave with these people.

• Although there are two verses to this song, the children will undoubtedly think of more. For example: some people can't write (draw, skate, skip) as well as or as fast as others. Use the words "well" or "fast" at your own discretion. However, always use "fast" with "at being friends." It is important not to interchange "well" and "fast" within the first three lines of each verse.

• Play and sing the song to the class. Once they are familiar with the song's musical form and words, have the children freely substitute additional verbs. Sometimes it may be necessary to substitute other words for "fast" or "well" (kick as high; throw as far, for example).

Note: In the last line of each verse, special attention should be given to the pauses after "fast" and "being." The pauses are there to emphasize the concept of the song.

Song #11: Some People

Song #12: When It Rains

Lyrics

All   When it rains, when it rains:
1st solo   **houses** get wet;
2nd solo   **cars** get wet;
3rd solo   **flowers** get wet;
4th solo   **dogs** get wet.
All   But when I have an umbrella,
  I — stay dry.

Children Required

entire class
4 soloists

Specific Skills and Concepts Developed

Cognitive: General Knowledge — *weather*
  Classification — *general category*
  Language — *vocabulary building, sentence building, plurals*

"When It Rains" deals with the concept of *weather* by presenting the most salient effect of rain: objects exposed to it get wet. The children classify objects in a *general category* by naming only those that may get wet when it rains. In addition, the last lines of the song suggest a means to avoid getting wet — using an umbrella.

Vocabulary building, sentence building, and *plurals* are developed and reinforced as the children sing first the original song and then its variations.

Procedure

• Discuss with the class what gets wet when it rains. The children should be able to name many things. As each child answers, encourage him or her to respond with a complete three-word sentence rather than with only a noun. These sentences form the nucleus of the lyrics for the song.

• Ask the class, "What happens when you have an umbrella?" The children will probably answer that they stay dry.

• Once the class is familiar with the song's musical form and words, have the children freely substitute additional objects that get wet for the solo responses.

Note: You may need to draw the children's attention to the lengthily sustained "I" in the last line of the song.

Variations

1. Discuss and sing about items that begin with specific speech sounds. For example: *c*ats, *c*ars, *c*ows, *c*abins.

2. Substitute snow for rain. For example:

When it snows, when it snows:
      ears get cold;
      noses get cold;
      hands get cold;
      feet get cold;
      But when I'm under the covers, I — stay warm.

Encourage the children to come up with their own suggestions for things that get cold and how to stay warm.

Song #12: When It Rains

Song #13: Today, Yesterday, and Tomorrow

	Lyrics	**Children Required**
All	Let's sing a song about today, yesterday, and tomorrow.	entire class
1st solo	Today is _____.	3 soloists
2nd solo	Yesterday was _____.	
3rd solo	And tomorrow will be _____.	
All	Today is _____.	
	Yesterday was _____.	
	And tomorrow will be _____.	

Specific Skills and Concepts Developed

Cognitive: General Knowledge — *progression of days of the week*
Language — *vocabulary building, sentence building*

"Today, Yesterday, and Tomorrow" focuses on the invariant *progression of days of the week.* Since the structure of the music does not allow for recitation of the seven days of the week, the child must develop the awareness that knowing today is Saturday, for instance, leads invariably to the conclusion that tomorrow is Sunday and yesterday was Friday.

Sentence building and *vocabulary building* are reinforced throughout the song by using complete sentences to name particular days of the week.

Procedure

• Ask the class, "What day is it today?" When the children answer, encourage them to begin with the words, "Today is _____." Then ask the same question for yesterday and tomorrow. Have the entire class repeat the three sentences several times. Doing so will help them learn the sequence of the days and the concept of the song. Also point out in your discussion the verbs "is," "was," and "will be," and their relationship to each other.

• Once the children have discussed what today is, yesterday was, and tomorrow will be, go over the lyrics marked All in the first and last sections of the song. They are basically the same, but you may find as the children sing the song that they become confused and forget the sequence of the words "today," "yesterday," and "tomorrow."

• Play and sing the song for the class.

• Once the children are familiar with the song's musical form and words, select 3 of them to sing the solo parts. At first, it may be a good idea to have the entire class sing the song. The solo parts may be substituted later, when the children become more proficient.

Note: Depending on the developmental level of the children, you may wish to repeat this song daily until a true concept of the sequence of days is well established.

In the first line of the song, the musical phrase for "today" is fun to sing in a sliding manner (a musical slur or legato).

In the last part marked *All,* pause after singing "Yesterday was _____."

Song #13: Today, Yesterday, and Tomorrow

Song #14: A Silly Song

Lyrics

All Here's a silly song.
It's not very long
Not a three-inch song.
Oh, that's much too long.
Just a one-inch song.
Solo If you're sitting up, are you sitting down?
All Yes. *(spoken)*
No. *(spoken)*
What a silly song to sing.
What a silly song to sing.

Children Required

entire class
1 soloist

Specific Skills and Concepts Developed

Cognitive: Language — *vocabulary building, word plays* or *puns.*

"A Silly Song" presents several *word plays* or *puns* and encourages *vocabulary building* by suggesting that the children think of others. By posing a question, the song requires the class to consider carefully the meanings of the words used, a technique that can extend the childrens' use of particular words and sharpen their concepts of words.

Procedure

• Ask the class the question in the solo, "If you're sitting up, are you sitting down?" This is, of course, a thought-provoking question that should stimulate much conversation. Some of the children will answer emphatically, "Yes." Others will answer just as emphatically, "No." They will then probably challenge each others' answers. The reasons given for disagreement may alter some children's initial thinking.

• In order to arrive at a definite "Yes" or "No," at some point you may find it necessary to ask, "Has anyone ever said to you, 'Sit up'?" The children will undoubtedly all agree, "Yes."

• It may be interesting to discuss the word play on "long" found in the first few lines of the song. Does one think of a song as being three inches long? One inch long? Of course not. But this is a **silly** song. It is just one inch long, not three inches long ("that's much too long"), so, "it's not very long."

• Play and sing the song to the class. At first, it may be a good idea for you to sing the question solo. Have the children decide beforehand whether the answer is "Yes" or "No."

• Once the class is familiar with the song, freely substitute additional puns for the question in the solo. Here are a few suggestions:

1. If the rain keeps up, will the rain come down? (In order for the children to arrive at a yes or no answer, you might give them a hint such as, "If the rain keeps up, we may have a flood." The children will then probably all agree that the answer is "Yes" to the above question.)
2. Can a running nose ever win a race?
3. Can a light bulb change to a heavy bulb?

Song #14: A Silly Song

Song #15: Sad Things

Lyrics

All Some things that happen are happy.
Some things that happen are sad.
Sad things happen to everyone sometimes.
Sad things happen to everyone sometimes.
Sad things happen to everyone.
Sad things happen sometimes.

Children Required

entire class

Specific Skills and Concepts Developed

Affective: Self-concept — *sad events*

"Sad Things" helps children put *sad events* in perspective. These events are emphasized as happening to everyone sometimes. Sad things are therefore universal experiences rather than personal experiences resulting from a deficiency or fault in the individual.

Procedure

• Open a discussion with your class about sad things by asking, "Have any of you ever had something happen to you that made you feel sad?" Then ask, "Can you think of something that happened that made you feel happy?" As the class volunteers answers, some of the children may wish to talk about what happened to them. Others may be reticent about things that are sad. Try to utilize words from the song during the discussion. ("Some things that happen are happy. Some things that happen are sad.") After the discussion is well underway, point out, "Sad things happen to everyone sometimes." Have the class repeat these sentences. They form the nucleus of the lyrics for the song.
• Play and sing the song to the class.

Note: The last two lines of the song, although very similar to the previous two, are sung more slowly, placing emphasis on different words.

You may need to caution the children about singing the word "sometimes" in the last line. Some children tend to sing this word too soon or too fast.

Song #15: Sad Things

some-times. Sad things hap - pen to ev - ery - one some - times.

Sad things hap - pen to ev - ery-one. Sad

things hap - pen some - times.

a tempo *riten.*

a tempo *riten.*

Song #16: Friends

Lyrics

All	Oh, I need a friend and you need a friend.
	We all need a friend to make us happy.
	I need a friend and you need a friend.
	We all need a friend.
Solo	You're my friend.
1st response	I'm your friend.
Solo	You're my friend.
2nd response	I'm your friend.
Solo	You're my friend.
3rd response	I' m your friend.
Solo	You're my friend. You're my friend.
4th response	I'm your friend.
Solo	You're my friend.
5th response	I'm your friend.
Solo	You're my friend.
6th response	I'm your friend.
All	Everybody needs a friend. Everybody needs a friend.

Children Required

entire class

1 soloist

Specific Skills and Concepts Developed

Cognitive: Language — *sentence building, pronouns, verbs, plurals, contractions*
Affective: Social Perception — *friends*

"Friends" is designed to foster the particular social perception of the need for *friends*. The structure of the song focuses on friends within the class, thus reinforcing the concept that we all need a friend to make us happy.

Sentence building, and the appropriate use *of pronouns, verb forms, plurals,* and *contractions* is practiced by the children as they sing first the original song and then its variations.

Procedures

Introduce this song by telling the class, "I need a friend and you need a friend. We all need a friend to make us happy." The children may wish to discuss with you who their friends are. As you have the children repeat the sentences above, stress the words "I," "you," and "we all" by pointing. These words are found in the lyrics marked *All* at the beginning of the song.

Next, shake a child's hand and say, "You're my friend." Ask the child to respond by saying, "I'm your friend." Continue doing this with other children until they get the idea of what to say when you shake their hands. Now have the entire class repeat the two sentences after you. These sentences form the nucleus of the lyrics for the rest of the song.

• Choose one child with a good voice to sing the solo, "You're my friend," to six classmates. Play and sing the song to the children.

• Do not select beforehand the children who will sing the six responses. Just remind the class that everyone should be ready to sing his or her part when given the cue. It is fun and adds challenge if children are called upon at random and by surprise.

Note: Special attention should be given to: Sustaining the word "need" just before the first solo. Sustaining the word "friends" in the solo after the third response

Song #16: Friends

48

Objectives

Educational objectives generally fall within two areas: the *cognitive* and the *affective*. Cognitive objectives relate to those functional skills and concepts that allow the individual to operate effectively within the environment. Language, reading, classification, mathematics, science, and reasoning skills and abilities all fall within the cognitive area. Affective objectives relate to those intra- and interpersonal skills and concepts that allow individuals to live comfortably with themselves and function in a world peopled with other individuals. Self-concept, personal attitudes and beliefs, and social perception fall within the affective area. The skills and concepts presented here are identified as being either cognitive or affective and are organized under these two headings.

Cognitive Skills and Concepts

The cognitive skills and concepts covered in the song activities include: *general knowledge* (information), *classification,* and *language.*

General Knowledge

The term "general knowledge" refers to a loose collection of concepts that children must acquire, at least at a rote level, during the early years of childhood. Personal information (name, address, age); the progression of days, months, and years; the identification of various types of weather; and the awareness of the five senses are examples of such concepts. General knowledge concepts serve two functions. First, they allow the child to deal with routine aspects of the environment, both social and natural, with a minimum amount of effort. Second, they serve as a foundation for the development of more complex concepts at a higher level and at a later time.

These songs foster four general knowledge concepts: *age, progression of days of the week, weather,* and *the five senses.*

Age. Personal information such as age contributes to the child's sense of identity and, ultimately, to the development of the self-concept. One song activity requires the child to think not only about how old he or she is, but also about how old others (brothers, sisters, or groups of children) are. As a result, the child becomes aware that age is a characteristic of all people.

Progression of Days of the Week. Too often primary-aged children learn the days of the week almost as a chant, beginning with Sunday and running nonstop to Saturday. The child who knows that today is Friday may be forced to go through the entire sequence to answer the simple question, "What day was yesterday?" The song activity about days of the week leads the child to view different days in progression. This discovery is a basic step in the development of the concept of time.

Weather. The initial awareness of weather conditions (rain, snow, wind, and their effects, for example) treated on a gross level eventually develops into more fully expanded concepts such as gradations in weather, sequences of weather conditions, ranges of effects, and so forth. Two song activities relating to concepts of weather heighten the child's awareness of different kinds of weather and prompt a variety of anticipatory responses to weather conditions.

The Five Senses. As children are made more aware of the five senses most of them have used since birth to explore the world, the senses may be viewed as useful "tools" associated with definite parts of the body. This leads to a more widely developed concept of the body as a composite whole made up of specialized parts performing particular, vital functions. One song activity focuses the child's attention on the potential means of exploring a specific thing. (For instance, you can hear music, but you can't taste, touch, smell, or see it.) Thus, the child is encouraged to carry on systematic, multi-sensory investigations of the environment.

Classification

Among the more important skills children acquire are classification skills. Children learn to classify by exploring the properties of objects, grouping them according to their common attributes, and then labeling all the objects in a particular group by responding about them in the same way (all are red; all are round; all are round and red, for example). Until children develop classification skills, they must remember every single attribute of an encountered object and the appropriate responses to it — a formidable memory task that ultimately becomes impossible.

Several songs foster classification skills by presenting *general* or *restricted categories* and asking the child to name objects that belong to those categories.

General and Restricted Categories. Some of the categories dealt with in the song activities are rather loose, allowing the child to choose objects that might be found in a house or classroom, for instance. Others are more restricted, requiring that the objects named be found in plurals, in a particular room of a house, and so forth. The most difficult categories presented in a few song variations are those involving properties such as color, hardness, and taste.

Language

In the early development of children, language fulfills a major function. It not only allows them to communicate effectively with others, but also plays a vital role in the growth of thought processes. As children acquire language, they begin to use words to label and describe objects, events, and relationships. Thus, language enables children to deal with their experiences on a cognitive level and to relate the experiences of the present to the past and the future.

Aspects of language development dealt with here include: *vocabulary building, sentence building, pronouns, subject-verb agreement, plurals, contractions, rhyming, past tense, word plays* or *puns, and initial sounds.* Because of the design of the songs and their variations, certain language skills receive particular emphasis as the children form musical responses. These include the appropriate use of pronouns, subject-verb agreement, and the use of plurals.

Vocabulary Building. Depending on the age, background, and experiences of the children, certain words in the song activities may be new to some members of your class. Group discussion combined with singing the songs should help those children to not only understand the meaning of unfamiliar words but also feel confident and comfortable when using them. For other children, the experience of hearing the words in a different context should reinforce vocabulary building.

Sentence Building. To truly communicate with others it is necessary that we be able to construct sentences. One- and two-word phrases, though possibly functional for communicating at a gross level, cannot express nuances of meaning, or more elaborate

50

thoughts. Furthermore, the ability to use sentences in oral communication is generally a prerequisite to written communication.

At home, and even at school, children frequently "get by" using extremely restricted communication patterns. ("Are you hungry?" — "Yes." "How old are you?" — "Seven." "What's six plus two?" — "Eight." "What day is today?" — "Monday."). These songs encourage sentence building and should improve the child's ability to form sentences. The format of the songs is such that the child's response is always a complete sentence.

Pronouns. Two types of pronouns are used in the song activities: nominative (I, you, he, she, we, they) and possessive (my, your, his, her, our, their). Whenever a variation of a song switches from a single-child response to a group response or from a group response to a single-child response, the pronouns in the song must be changed accordingly. Before singing a variation, the children should be asked how the words of the song must be altered to suit the new situation.

Subject-Verb Agreement. Because the English language specifies that different verb forms be used with subjects differing in person or in number, the use of certain song variations require changes in the verbs. For example, when the referent in a song is single ("he"/"she") and is then substituted by a plural ("they"), the verb must be changed to agree with the subject ("has" to "have" or "is" to "are" for example).

Plurals. Several of the song activities and their variations necessitate the use of plural nouns. Some songs call for plural nouns in the responses; others suggest substituting a plural noun for a singular noun.

A number of children consistently drop the "s" from plural nouns. To the degree that it is possible, you should listen carefully to the children's pronunciation of nouns that pluralize regularly to make sure that the final "s" is being sounded.

Contractions. Whether or not a child personally chooses to *use* contractions, if the child wishes to converse with others or to read books others have written, he or she must be able to *process* contractions. It is necessary, then, that the child be able to decode common contractions into their two-word equivalents. One of the song activities is designed specifically to present contractions to the class. Other songs offer additional practice using contractions by incorporating them into the lyrics.

Rhyming. Rhymes not only are fun for children, but also contribute in several ways to their development. The ability to recognize and name words that sound alike serves as a basis for building and extending word attack or word analysis skills. In one of the song activities, for example, the fact that the word "way" is like "day" except that it starts with a different speech sound, provides the child with clues to pronounce the word. Similarly, knowing that "say" sounds like "day" provides clues to spell "say" (assuming, of course, that the child knows how to spell "day").

Knowledge of rhymes contributes to the aesthetic development of the child, as well. Rhyme is a key element in many great poems and songs. An awareness of rhymes adds a new dimension to the child's appreciation of these literary forms.

Past Tense of Verbs. English, like many other languages, distinguishes past and present events by the use of different verb forms. Furthermore, this distinction has been regularized to a certain extent by designating that the past tense of many verbs be formed by adding "ed" to the present tense.

Most children learn such language rules with little apparent effort during preschool years. Some children, however, may come from backgrounds where the conventions of language differ from the "standard English" that prevails in schools. Other children, especially those with learning problems, may simply need systematic exposure to the past tense/present tense distinction. The specific purpose of one of the song activities is to provide such systematic practice. Within this song the children take a verb in the present tense and change it to the past tense.

Word Plays or Puns. Envisioning a class of punning children may make you wince and question whether puns are educationally valid. Puns capitalize on words that sound the same but have different meanings, or alternate meanings of the same word. The question format of one of the song activities presents plays on words and encourages the child to think of others. This playful approach enables children to consider words and their meanings in a new and different light. Of possibly even greater benefit, however, is the realization that words can be more than functional; they can be enjoyed, savored, and used with relish.

Initial Sounds. One of the most important pre-reading skills the child must master is the association of letters with their sounds. Learning the distinct sounds for various letters allows the child to analyze unfamiliar words he or she may encounter. Word analysis, however, requires more than simply knowing the appropriate sound for each letter in a word. It also requires noting the position of each letter so that sounds can be made in sequence. Thus, most developmental reading programs pay much attention to the beginning, middle, and final sounds of words.

The variations of several song activities are designed to provide practice with initial sounds. All the variations ask the children to name objects that fit a particular category (things in a house, things you eat, and so forth) and that begin with a particular speech sound. To accomplish this, the children must first consider objects that belong in the category and then analyze their names to determine whether the words begin with the appropriate sounds. This dual task may prove very difficult for certain children and should only be introduced after classification skills are well established.

Affective Skills and Concepts

The affective skills and concepts presented in the song activities for this program include: *self concept* and *social perception.*

Self-concept

The self-concept is, essentially, the way an individual views himself or herself. Furthermore, the self-concept serves as a filter through which the individual perceives and interacts with the world. Aspects of the self-concept dealt with through the songs presented here are: *identity, positive self-concept, mistakes,* and *sad events.*

Identity and **Positive Self-concept.** In respect to the self-concept, "identity" refers to a person's basic understanding of who he or she is. Identity develops from the individual's experiences within the environment. During their early years, children begin to apply certain labels to themselves that identify them as persons called by particular names; living in particular houses or apartments; having red, black, or blond hair, and so forth. As the child develops skills, as he or she learns to walk, run, jump, sing, or read, for example, the concept of the self expands to include new labels such as walker, runner, jumper, singer, or reader.

Later, the child becomes aware of values and starts making judgments. Some of the judgments are applied to the self, and thus the view of the self becomes more qualified. For example, viewing the self as simply a runner and reader may change to viewing the self as a *good* runner and a *poor* reader as the child judges his or her relative abilities in those areas. If many of the self judgments are negative, the child may come to view the entire self negatively.

Crucial to the individual's growth into a fully functioning being is the development of a flexible, expansive, positive self-concept. If an individual's self-concept is rigid, limited, or negative, then his or her perceptions and experiences will probably be the same. Children who view themselves as failures at certain tasks may resist or avoid situations presenting those tasks. In addition, a child who has encountered much failure in a particular setting such as school, may approach similar settings with the assumption that he or she will certainly fail again.

Several of the song activities are designed to expand the child's basic identity and to enhance various aspects of the self-concept. Skillful use of the songs should help children view themselves in a positive way.

Mistakes and **Sad Events.** Frequently, children feel that mistakes are "bad" and that sad events are the result of some fault in the individual. Two song activities help put mistakes and sad events in perspective by presenting them as experiences that happen to everyone sometimes. Thus, one is not bad for making a mistake, or necessarily at fault for a sad event taking place.

Social Perception

The term "social perception" refers to the individual's ability to understand the feelings and viewpoints of others. Initially, children are very egocentric and perceive situations from only a limited standpoint colored by their own feelings, needs, and desires. As children develop, however, and come in contact with increasing numbers of other people, they begin to realize that the feelings, needs, and desires of others may conflict with their own. Such encounters force the child to take into account differences between his or her personal views and the views of others. Through such conflict the child is made increasingly aware of alternate perspectives and develops insights into the feelings and viewpoints of other people.

The particular areas of social perception fostered are: *friends, mistakes of others,* and *individual differences*.

Friends. The need for friends and the fact that all people are capable of making friends are important concepts that affect the individual's social behavior. Two of the song activities stress these concepts and encourage children to think about what makes friends and who their friends are.

Mistakes of Others. The awareness that everybody makes mistakes sometimes is as vital to social perception as it is to the self-concept. The same song activity used to support the self concept of mistakes stresses that making mistakes is a universal experience rather than a personal one, and should thus encourage children to be tolerant of the mistakes of others.

Individual Differences. Because schools are rapidly accommodating a greater number of students with a wide range of intellectual, physical, and sensory abilities, the child's acceptance of individual differences among people is becoming increasingly important. Too often the only comments made to children about individual differences and/or handicaps are admonishments: "Don't stare at handicapped persons"; "Don't laugh at those who are slow"; or "Be kind to those who are different." As a result, obvious handicaps can be very disconcerting to children. They may fear that they, too, will become handicapped, or think that a handicap is punishment for some transgression. They may simply feel uncomfortable around handicapped persons because their natural curiosity concerning handicaps is in conflict with the warning not to stare or laugh.

The last song activity in this music program deals directly with individual differences and opens the way for candid discussions concerning them. Such discussions also should consider ways in which people are alike and should emphasize that all people are potential friends.

OTHER MUSIC BOOKS
FOR
CHILDREN
from
Barcelona Publishers

Snow White:
A Guide to Child-Centered Musical Theatre

Patricia Rickard-Lauri, Harriet Groeschel, Clive Robbins,
Carol Robbins, Michelle Ritholz and Alan Turry

A beautiful book providing everything needed to teach and direct a children's production of *Snow White*. Included are the story, a play version, a musical score, production notes, and a compact disk for the actual performance. No parts or extra copies are needed! The story is a simplified adaptation of Grimm's fairy tale, presented with exquisite color ink drawings of actual children who have performed the play. The story is accompanied by a glossary defining the more difficult words, and suggestions on how to present the story to the children. The play is a formal script consisting of a narrative, dialogue, stage and lighting cues, and music directives. The score contains all the music and songs in the sequence in which they are to be performed. For those groups without an accomplished pianist, an audio CD is included with both voice and instrumental renditions of each song. Depending on the scope of the production, the entire score may or may not be used. The production notes provide a guide for how to use the play, suggestions for costume and set design, and a complete child-centered approach for preparing the children to participate. Though originally developed for children with special needs, this play and guide can bring the joys of musical theatre to children of all ability levels.

(ISBN 0-9624080-6-9 • Paperback with CD: $68.00)

Learning Through Music
Herbert Levin and Gail Levin

A collection of 42 musical activities designed for classroom teachers, music teachers, and music therapists to use in their work with children of various ages, abilities, and needs at the primary level. With over 100 variations, involving singing, moving, and playing instruments, these developmentally sequenced activities have been carefully crafted to help children develop: perceptual motor abilities, attentional skills, behavioral limits, speech and language skills, and relational concepts. The music is superb, the piano accompaniments are easy, the activities are great fun for the children, and each one comes with complete instructions on how to engage children at various levels of difficulty. Inasmuch as this is a reprinting of the Levin's highly acclaimed original work of the same title, the effectiveness of these activities has already been demonstrated in various settings.

(ISBN 1-891278-00-2 • Paperback: $28.00)